In the name of God, the Lord of Mercy, the Giver of Mercy

To all the curious kids. May you enjoy life's adventures.

Lunar Learners LLC
52 Lakeshore Plaza, Suite E
Kirkland, WA 98033

www.LunarLearners.com

First Edition

ISBN 978-1-7336351- 4-1

Library of Congress Control Number: 2019902098

The Adventures of Nuh's Ark

(Peace Be Upon Him)

Written by Khadijah Khaki
Illustrated by Tashna Salim

Lunar Learners LLC

Drill! Bang! Screw!

"What's all that noise? We're trying to sleep here," grumbled the koala.

"This is no time to sleep. Aren't you coming?" said the zebra hastily.
"Coming where?"

Nuh's building a....

"What did he say?" asked the koala,
as he perked up.
"I think he said park," groaned the tortoise.
"Park? I want to come!" said the sheep excitedly.

"No silly, he said ark...as in boat,"
exclaimed the giraffe.
"A boat! We're going to a boat!...wait...
why are we going to a boat?" the koalas asked,
still confused.

"But why an ark?
I don't do so well in small spaces."

"I heard it will be raining cats and dogs,"
the gecko informed.
"What?!" barked the dog.
"It is just an expression for lots of rain,"
clarified the cat.

"Oh dear, I did not see rain in the forecast.
I'm not dressed for rain," the koala said,
looking concerned.
"Hopefully it's just a light sprinkle."

"Sorry, 40 nights and days of rain,"
sighed the alligator.

"40?" cried the panda.
"That's a big number. I can only count to 10."

"I can't keep up," the koala complained as he stopped to catch his breath.
"Can we hitch a ride?"

"So, what have you heard about this ark?"
"I'm just going for the free food,"
grunted the hippo.
"Did someone say free food?"
drooled the squirrel.
"This just keeps getting better."

"I hope they have blueberries,"
 growled the bear.
"And bananas," giggled the monkey.

"And burgers," said the tiger as he licked his lips.

"You kids are always hungry,"
 sighed the owl as he swooped past.

"Let me get this straight," began the koala as he scratched his head.
"God is going to make it rain for 40 nights and days, so He asked Nuh to build an ark for all of us?"

"That's right," replied the horse. "God is not happy with the way people are behaving, so He wants us to start a new life. He will save the animals and people who will listen to Him and come on the ark with Nuh."

"Well we definitely want to be on Nuh's ark!"
"Let's go!"

It rained for 40 nights and days,
as Nuh's ark sailed away.
Sometimes fast and sometimes slow,
with all the animals in tow.

As the waves soared,
the lions roared.

The cheetahs leaped,
which scared the sheep.

Although, hard at times, they helped
each other and stayed true,
for they knew that God would
help them through.

Then, at last they saw a light.
From left to right was all God's truth,
and all His might.
The greenest grass they had ever seen
and the fruits and flowers of their dreams.

Nuh's faith in God had lead them to this day.

And each of them was on their journey,
to live a life in God's way.

Made in the USA
Monee, IL
26 May 2020